The Mini Soccer Rule Book Quiz

The Mini Soccer Rule Book Quiz

Ernest Henry

Drawings by Mauro Golin

QuizMaster Reg Spicer

Published in Great Britain in 2002
Talking Pig
PO Box 29769 London NW3 3ZU

First Published in 2002
Copyright (c) Text Ernest Henry 2002
Copyright (c) Illustrations Mauro Golin 2002
The moral right of the author has been asserted
The moral right of the Illustrator has been asserted
A CIP catalogue record of this book is available from the British Library

ISBN 1 903520 04 5

Designed by Nadine Aroyo

Printed in Great Britain by Turnergraphic

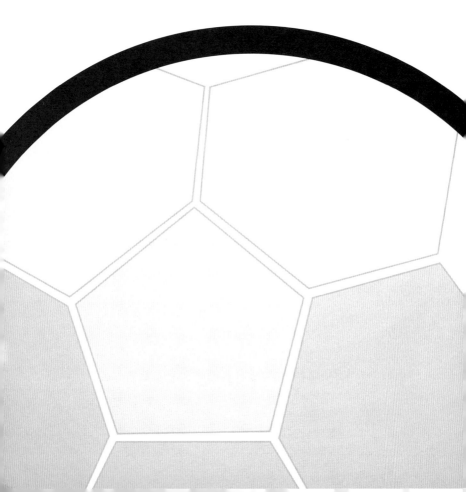

Dedicated to *The Beautiful Game*

The Score

Introduction

So - you want to play Mini Soccer?

Yeah - you all scream and shout. Fab! Great! Bad! Good! Left! Right! So coo-el... what is it???

Well - what indeed. You have to know what a game's all about before you start playing it, otherwise you could be dribbling (no - not from the mouth, you daft prune) when you should be shooting, keeping the ball when you should be passing and swerving all over the place when you should be firmly guarding your goal. And that ain't cricket!

Or even football.

Or even Mini Soccer.

So this book is for YOU!!

It's based on the Rules of Mini Soccer - or the LAWS OF MINI SOCCER as the Football Association likes to call them.

And this is the most fun way of learning something about the fastest growing game in the Wooooooorld!

Mini Soccer - it's all about speed, split-second decisions and skill. Knowing what you're doing also helps! So make sure you do know what you're doing - and just as importantly, make sure everyone else who's involved in your game also knows what *they* are doing.

First off, you need a Referee, a Manager, a Mum or Dad, relatives or friends, and other kids to play with.

The Ref should know what's going on; your Manager may not know what time of day it is, he's been so busy organising all your fixtures for the past twelve weeks! And dear old Mum and Dad probably won't have a clue. But by watching you, they'll start to get the idea. Be patient!

OK. To start with, take one ball. A football would be handy, but even then, there are different sizes. If you're under 8, you need a Size 3 football, otherwise use a Size 4.

Next, find a Ref. He's the one who runs after everyone blowing a whistle, looking at his watch and throwing coloured cards all over the place if you've been a naughty little Becksy!

He likes to be called Ref (or Sir!), but nobody ever does, so just call him Dad!

Then, pick a team of players for each side. Boys, girls, boys and girls, girls and boys. And bananas. Bananas are very good for energy boosts.

Your dream team should have

A Striker
A Goalie
Defenders
But how many of each ??
A banana.

Now, appoint your Manager. He should know a thing or two about organising things. (Mum would be great??? OK, it's only an idea!)

The Manager's job is

- ⚡ to organise training sessions
- ⚡ to organise somewhere for you to play
- ⚡ someone for you to play with
- ⚡ a time and date to have the match

- ⚡ to get you all together
- ⚡ to get you to the match
- ⚡ to get you back
- ⚡ buying juice and bikkies for half time
- ⚡ to be generally bossy and **GET THINGS DONE.**

BIG IMPORTANT REMINDER. Be sure to have some decent kit.

Do try and look like Becks and not like Posh, unless you're a girl, in which case the reverse is true... only in footie gear and not some slinky out to a party fancy flouncy hip hop drop dead gorgeous dancing prancing having a lovely time and this party is great and isn't Robbie Williams cool and so is Darren... Who's Darren?

You are now all assembled.

Team
Manager
Ref
Ball
Somewhere to play on.
Something to play in.
Someone to play with.
Another team to play against
Something to drink at half time.

Bananas...

And - what do you do ???

Well, what you do is governed by the Rules - or
Laws of Mini Soccer - as written by the Football
Association (as we said before - just checking
you're not falling asleep!). Remember, Mini Soccer
is Real Football, and to help you understand the
Laws, this Quiz Book will show you the way.

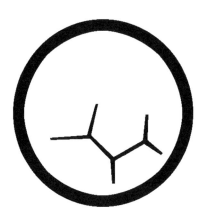

Right-o, off we go!

Getting Started

There are 17 Laws of Mini Soccer and these were issued by the Football Association in 2001. The first 4 Laws define what the pitch should look like, what you play with, how many should be in each team and what you should wear.

Each question has a reference to one or more of these 17 MINI SOCCER LAWS and we've identified them like this

L1= Law 1
L2= Law 2
L10=Law 10 ...and so on

Before we start the quiz, you need to know that **Each** side has

Forwards
Defenders
A goalkeeper ...and, sometimes, Mid-
fielders

Each Question has a number of suggested answers and we give you a clue how many correct answers there are - there's always **ONE**, but sometimes more.

To choose the answer(s) you think is (are) correct, take a sticky ball from the back of the book and stick it on the ball drawn next to your chosen answer. Once you've completed all the questions, check the answers at the back of the book (no peeking!) and see how many you've scored correctly by placing your sticky ball on the corresponding answer!

You can tell how well you've done and how much you know by checking your **Score on Page 132.**

A few things to remember...

Measurements are given in yards.

The mini soccer pitch is smaller than a full sized one, but gets larger the more players you have.

You're given a clue as to how many correct answers there are to each question.

Here's a sample quizzie question to show you how the Rule Book Quiz works.

Question 1

What is the minimum size of the pitch (in yards) for Under 7's and 8's?

There's only **ONE** answer.
It refers to L1 (Law 1).

Is it

a) 20 x 30

b) 30 x 40

c) 30 x 50

d) 40 x 60

The correct answer is **a),** but don't worry if you got it wrong because this Quiz will help you learn the Rules.

So lets try a few more questions...

Question 2

What is the maximum size of the pitch (in yards) for Under 7's and 8's?
There is only **ONE** answer.
It refers to L1.

Is it

a) 20 x 30

b) 30 x 40

c) 30 x 50

d) 40 x 60

Question 3

What is the minimum size of the pitch (in yards) for Under 9's and 10's?
There is only **ONE** answer.
It refers to L1.

Is it

a) 20 x 30

b) 30 x 40

c) 30 x 50

d) 40 x 60

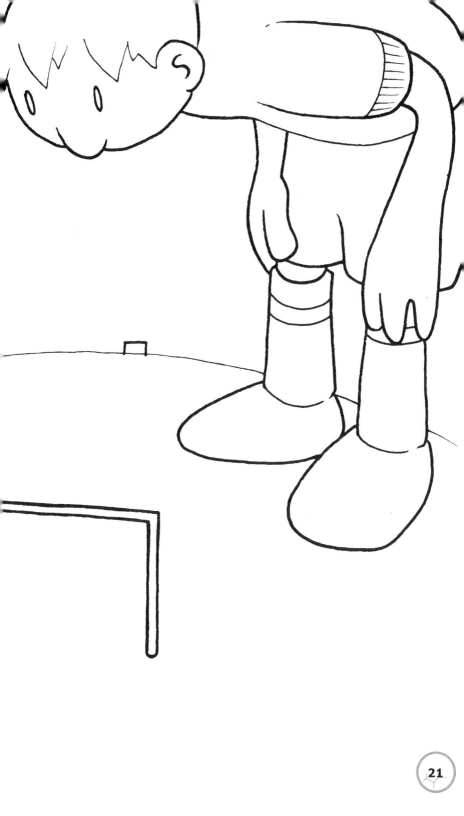

Question 4

What is the maximum size of the pitch for Under 9's and 10's? There is only **ONE** answer.
It refers to L1.

Is it

a) 20 x 30

b) 30 x 40

c) 30 x 50

d) 40 x 60

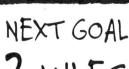

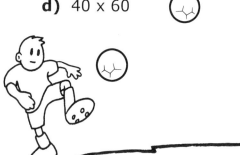

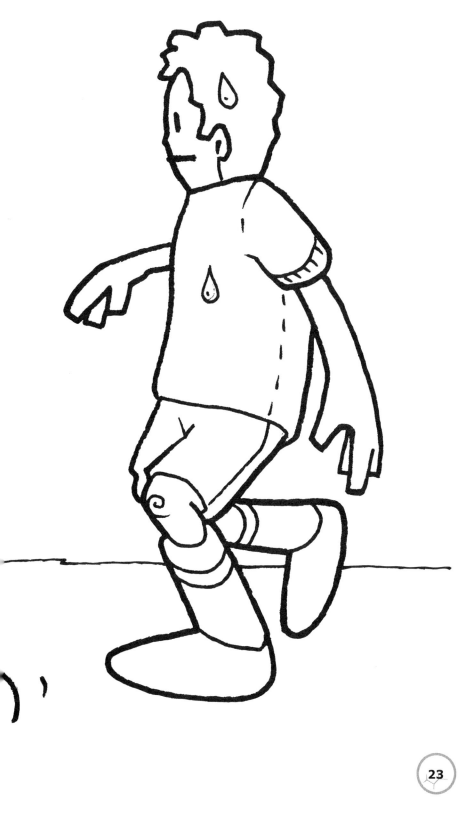

Question 5

Your pitch needs a Penalty Area. This is the same for all age-groups playing mini soccer, but how big should it be?
There is only **ONE** answer.
It refers to L1.

Is it
(in yards)

a) 6 x 12

b) 8 x 15

c) 10 x 18

d) 12 x 20

Question 6

Now that you've got your Penalty Area, you need a goal at each end. This is the same for all age-groups playing mini soccer, but how big should it be?
There is only **ONE** answer.
It refers to L1.

Is it
(in feet)

a) 5 x 10

b) 6 x 12

c) 7 x 16

d) 8 x 24

Question 7

Your Goal needs a penalty spot. This is the same for all age-groups playing mini soccer, but how far should it be from the goal line? There is only **ONE** answer.
It refers to L1.

Is it
(in yards)

a) 6

b) 8

c) 10

d) 12

Question 8

Now you are ready to play. How many players in each team?

There are **TWO** answers to each part of this question. They refer to L3.

For Under 7s – 8s

Is it

a) 4

b) 5

c) 6

d) 7

For Under 9s – 10s

Is it

a) 4

b) 5

c) 6

d) 7

Question 9

What is the maximum squad size?
There is **ONE** answer.
It refers to L3.

Is it

a) 8

b) 10

c) 12

d) double the team size

Question 10

How many substitutes can play?
There is **ONE** answer.
It refers to L3.

Is it

a) 1

b) 2

c) 3

d) as many as you like

Question 11

When can a substitution be made?
There are **TWO** answers.
They refer to L3.

Are they

a)   any time

b)   with permission from the referee or game leader

c)   whenever your manager wants to

d)   during a stoppage in play

Question 12

If you are substituted, can you return to the same game later on?
There is **ONE** answer.
It refers to L3.

Is it

a) yes

b) no

Question 13A

What must you wear, as a player?
There are **TWO** answers.
They refer to L4.

Should you wear

a) high heeled shoes

b) stockings

c) football boots

d) football shirt

e) football shorts

f) socks

g) gloves

h) shin pads

i) coat

j) a distinguishing playing strip

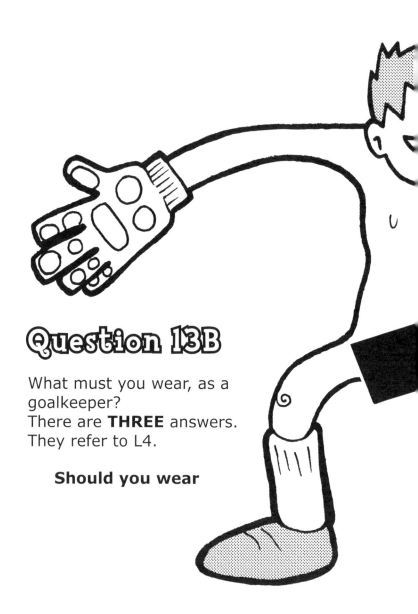

Question 13B

What must you wear, as a goalkeeper?
There are **THREE** answers.
They refer to L4.

Should you wear

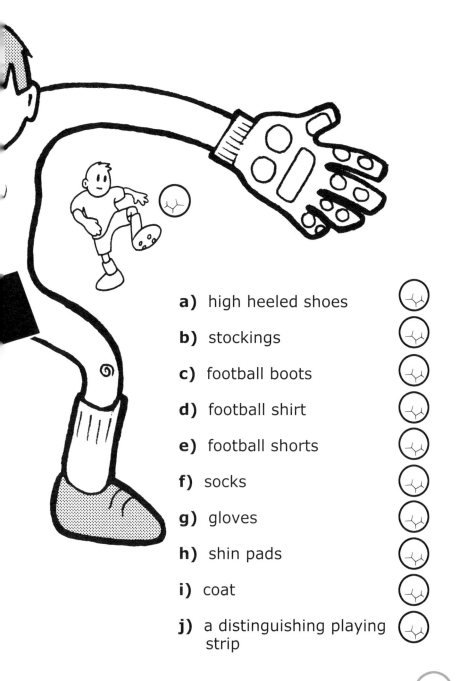

a) high heeled shoes

b) stockings

c) football boots

d) football shirt

e) football shorts

f) socks

g) gloves

h) shin pads

i) coat

j) a distinguishing playing strip

Questions 14

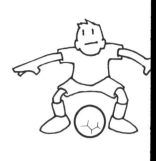

Who enforces the Laws of the Game?
There is **ONE** answer.
It refers to L5.

Is It

a) my manager

b) my dad

c) the referee

THAT W[

Question 15

Can the referee stop play if

a) I am too tired

b) my dad wants me to have a drink

c) he thinks there has been a foul

d) a dog runs onto the pitch

There are **TWO** answers.
They refer to L5.

Question 16

Can the referee stop play if

a) I am too tired

b) my dad starts arguing with him

c) there is a serious injury

d) I get a nose bleed

There are **THREE** answers.
They refer to L5.

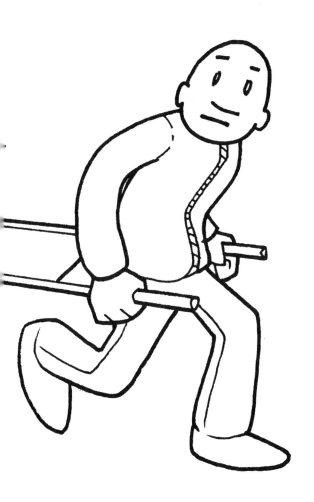

Question 17

Can the referee stop play if

a) I have a runny nose

b) my manager swears at him

c) a players wound is bleeding

There are **TWO** answers.
They refer to L5.

Question 18

Can the referee change his mind?
There is **ONE** answer.
It refers to L5.

a) yes

b) no

c) yes, provided play has not restarted

Question 19

Can the referee play on, even if there has been a foul?
There is **ONE** answer.

It refers to L5.

Is it

a) yes

b) no

c) yes, if he thinks it gives advantage
to the team fouled.

Question 20

If a referee plays advantage, can he change his mind if advantage does not ensue?
There is **ONE** answer.
It apples to L5.

Is it

a) yes

b) no

Question 21

Must the referee have assistant referees?
There is **ONE** answer.
It refers to L6.

Is it

a) yes

b) no

Question 22

Who can be nominated to assist the referee?
There are **FOUR** answers.
They all refer to L6.

Are they

a) me

b) my dad

c) my dog

d) my manager

e) anybody

Question 23

Can I play as much mini soccer as I like in any day?
There is **ONE** answer.
It refers to L7.

Is it

a) yes

b) no

Question 24

What is the recommended number of
minutes play each half?
There is **ONE** answer for each set of ages.
It refers to L7.

Is it

Under 7s & 8s

a) 5

b) 10

c) 15

d) 20

Under 9s & 10s

a) 5

b) 10

c) 15

d) 20

Question 25

Is there a maximum half time interval?
There is **ONE** answer.
This refers to L7.

Is it

a) yes

b) no

Question 26

What is the maximum half time interval?
There is **ONE** answer.
This refers to L7.

Is it

a) 5 minutes

b) 10 minutes

c) 15 minutes

Question 27

How long may I play in any one day?
There is **ONE** answer for each age group.
This refers to L7.

Is it

Under 7s & 8s

a) 45 minutes

b) 60 minutes

c) 90 minutes

d) as long as I like

Under 9s & 10s

a) 45 minutes

b) 60 minutes

c) 90 minutes

d) as long as I like

Question 28

When we kick-off, where must the ball go?
There is **ONE** answer.
This refers to L8.

Is it

a) forwards

b) backwards

c) anywhere

Question 29

At kick-off, how far away must the opponents be?
There is **ONE** answer.
This refers to L8.

Is it

a) 5 yards

b) 8 yards

c) 10 yards

Question 30

When may a dropped ball be used to restart play?
There is **ONE** answer.
This refers to L8.

Is it

a) when play was temporarily stopped by the referee, without a foul being committed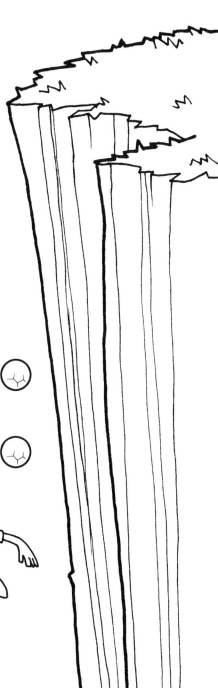

b) whenever the referee feels like it

Question 31

Where should a dropped ball usually be taken? There is **ONE** answer. This refers to L8.

Is it

a) where play was temporarily stopped by the referee

b) wherever the referee feels like it

Question 32

Where should a dropped ball be taken, where play was stopped in the penalty area?
There is **ONE** answer.
It refers to L8.

Is it

a) where play was temporarily stopped by the referee

b) from the penalty line, parallel with the goal line, nearest to where play was stopped.

c) wherever the referee feels like it

UIT.

Question 33

When is the ball out of play?
There are **TWO** answers.
They refer to L9.

Are they

a) when play is stopped by the referee

b) when most of the ball crosses the goal line or touch line

c) when all of the ball crosses the goal line or touch line

BASICALLY, Y
THE BALL AND

Question 34

Does the offside rule apply?
There is **ONE** answer.
This refers to L11.

Is it

a) yes

b) no

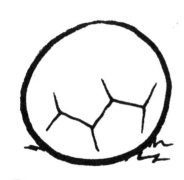

Question 35

What type of free kicks can the referee award?
There is **ONE** answer.
This refers to L12.

Is it

a) direct

b) indirect

c) either

Question 36

If I kick an opponent

      or   attempt to kick an opponent
      or   trip an opponent
      or   attempt to trip an opponent
      or   jump at an opponent
      or   charge an opponent
      or   strike an opponent
      or   attempt to strike an opponent
      or   push an opponent

should a free kick be awarded against me?

There is **ONE** answer.
This refers to L12.

Is it

a) yes

b) no

c) only if I was careless, reckless or
    using excessive force

Question 37

If I make contact with an opponent before touching the ball

- or hold an opponent
- or spit at an opponent
- or handle the ball deliberately
- or play dangerously
- or impede the progress of an opponent
- or prevent their goalkeeper from releasing the ball from his/her hands,

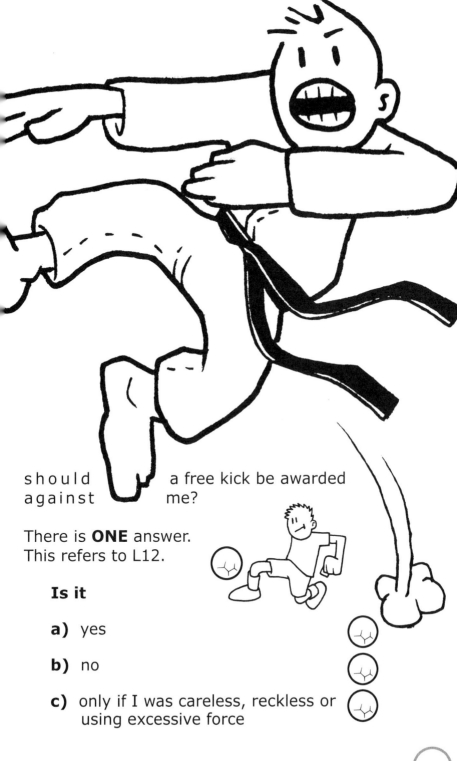

should a free kick be awarded against me?

There is **ONE** answer. This refers to L12.

Is it

a) yes

b) no

c) only if I was careless, reckless or using excessive force

Question 38

If a foul was awarded against me for one of the offences shown in Q36 or Q37 and the offence occurred in our penalty area, should a penalty kick be given?

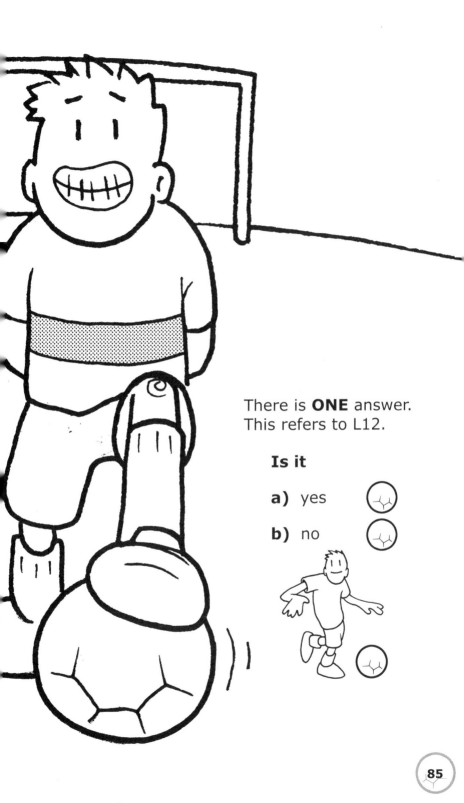

There is **ONE** answer.
This refers to L12.

Is it

a) yes

b) no

Question 39

If a foul was awarded against me for one of the offences shown in Q36 or Q37 and the offence occurred in our penalty area, should a penalty kick be given even if the ball was not in the penalty area at the time?

There is **ONE** answer.
This refers to L12.

Is it

a) yes

b) no

Question 40

Must a penalty kick always be awarded for a foul in the penalty area?
There is **ONE** answer.
This refers to L12.

Is it

a) yes

b) no

Question 41

What should be awarded if the goalkeeper, in his/her penalty area,

 takes more than 6 seconds to release the ball from his/her hands

or

 handles the ball again, after releasing it before it has touched another player

or

 handles the ball after it has been deliberately kicked to him/her by a team mate

or

 handles the ball directly after a throw in by a team mate?

There is **ONE** answer.
This refers to L12.

Is it

a) penalty kick

b) free kick

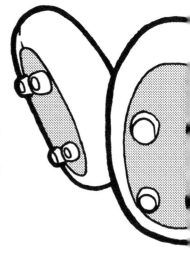

Question 42

Where should a free kick be taken, if awarded for a foul in the penalty area?

There is **ONE** answer.
This refers to L12.

Is it

a) where the offence occurred

b) from the penalty spot

c) from the penalty area line, parallel with the goal line, nearest to where the offence occurred

Question 43

What colour card will I get for

- ⚡ unsporting behaviour
- ⚡ dissent
- ⚡ persistant infringement of the rules
- ⚡ delaying the restart of the game
- ⚡ being less than 5 yards from the ball when our opponets restart play
- ⚡ coming onto the pitch without permission
- ⚡ leaving the pitch without permission

There is **ONE** answer.
This refers to L12.

Is it

a) red ◯

b) yellow ◯

c) none ◯

Question 44

What colour card will I get for

- ⚡ serious foul play
- ⚡ violent conduct
- ⚡ spitting at anybody
- ⚡ offensive, insulting or abusive language and/or gestures
- ⚡ fouling an opponent who has an obvious goal scoring opportunity
- ⚡ deliberately handling the ball, denying the opposing team an obvious goal scoring opportunity
- ⚡ a second yellow card

There is **ONE** answer.
This refers to L12.

Is it

a) red

b) yellow

c) none

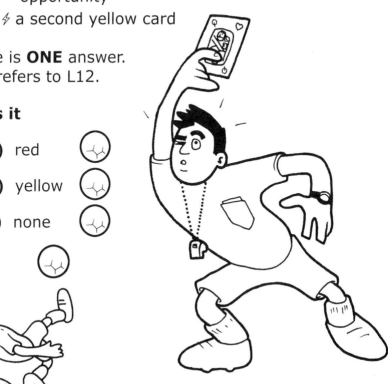

٩٦.

Question 45

As an opponent, how far from the ball must I be from a free kick or a corner kick?

There is **ONE** answer.
This refers to L13 and L17.

Is it

a) 2 yards

b) 5 yards

c) 10 yards

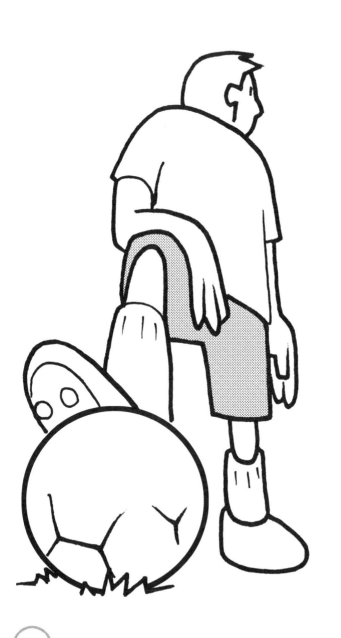

Question 46

Except for the defending goalkeeper, how far must all players be from the ball when a penalty kick is taken?

There are **TWO** answers.
They refer to L14.

Are they

a) 2 yards

b) 5 yards

c) 10 yards

d) outside the penalty area

Question 47

Which direction must the ball go from a penalty kick?

There is **ONE** answer.
This refers to L14.

Is it

a) forwards

b) backwards

c) any direction I like

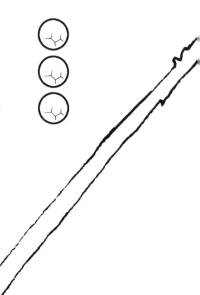

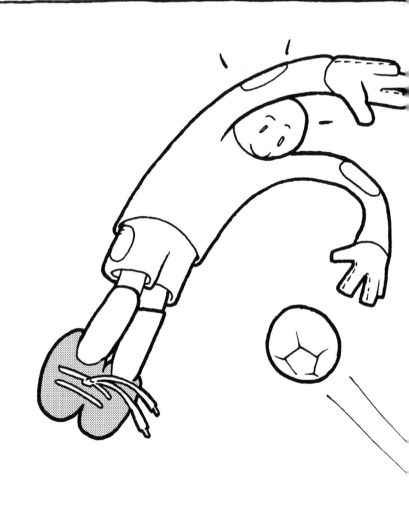

Question 48

If my side scores a goal from a penalty kick, but I committed an offence while it was being taken, what should the referee do?

There is **ONE** answer.
This refers to L14.

Is it

a) award a goal

b) take the penalty kick again

c) disallow the goal, and award a goal kick.

Question 49

If the opposition scores a goal from a penalty kick, but I committed an offence while it was being taken, what should the referee do?

There is **ONE** answer.
This refers to L14.

Is it

a) award a goal

b) take the penalty kick again

c) disallow the goal, and award a goal kick.

Question 50

If the opposition misses a goal from a penalty kick, but I committed an offence while it was being taken, what should the referee do?

There is **ONE** answer.
This refers to L14.

Is it

a) award a goal

b) take the penalty kick again

c) disallow the goal, and award a goal kick.

Question 51

If both teams commit an offence while a penalty kick is being taken, what should the referee do?

There is **ONE** answer.
This refers to L14.

Is it

a) award a goal

b) take the penalty kick again

c) disallow the goal, and award a goal kick.

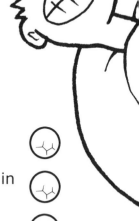

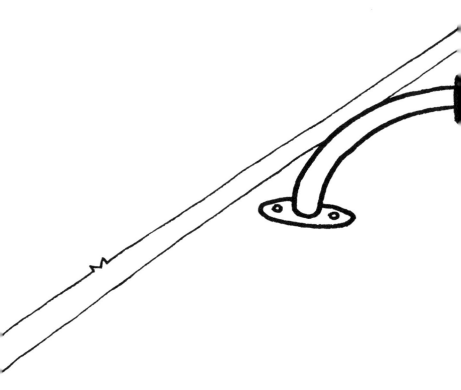

Question 52

From a throw in, the thrower should

    a) face the field of play

    b) have part of each foot on the touch line, or on the ground outside the touchline

    c) have all of each foot on the touch line, or on the ground outside the touchline

d) use both hands

e) throw the ball from behind and over their head.

There are **FOUR** answers. These refer to L15.

Question 53

From a throw in, what happens if I try to throw the ball along the line, but it doesn't come into play?

There is **ONE** answer.
This refers to L15.

Is it

a) the referee should award a
throw in to the opposition

b) the referee should award a free
kick to the opposition

c) the referee should let me take it
again

Question 54

From a throw in, or a corner kick, what happens if the ball doesn't go far enough and I kick it to one of my team mates?

There is **ONE** answer.
This refers to L15 + L17.

Is it

a) the referee should award a throw in to the opposition

b) the referee should award a free kick to the opposition

c) the referee should let me take it again

Question 55

Who can take a goal kick?

There is **ONE** answer.
This refers to L16.

Is it

a) our goal keeper

b) any player in our team

Question 56

Where must a goal kick be taken?

There is **ONE** anwer.
This refers to L16.

Is it

a) from the goal line

b) from the penalty area line

c) from anywhere within the penalty area

Question 57

Where must the opponents be when a goal kick is taken?

There are **TWO** answers.
This refers to L16.

Is it

a) anywhere they like

b) at least 5 yards from the ball

c) outside the penalty area

Question 58

An opponent, who was 5 yards from the ball when we took a goal kick, runs into the penalty area and gets the ball before us. What should the referee do?

There are **TWO** answers.
These refer to L16.

Should he

a) do nothing ◯

b) wave play on ◯

c) give us a free kick ◯

d) ask us to take the goal kick again ◯

Answers

Q   A   Goal ...

1 . . . . a)

2 . . . . c)

3 . . . . c)

4 . . . . d)

5 . . . . c)

6 . . . . b)

Check these answers against the ones you've marked with a Sticky Footie Sticker!

Once you've answered all the questions, and checked your answers, add up all the correct ones.

. Missed

7 . . . . b) ⚽

8 . . . a) & b) Under 7s & 8s ⚽ ⚽

c) & d) Under 9s & 10s ⚽ ⚽

9 . . . . d) ⚽

10 . . . . d) ⚽

11 . . . . b) & d) ⚽ ⚽

12 . . . . a) ⚽

13A . . . . b) & h) ⚽ ⚽

13B . . . . b) ,h) & j) ⚽ ⚽ ⚽

14 . . . . c) ⚽

15 . . . . c) & d) ⚽ ⚽

16 . . . . b) c) d) ⚽ ⚽ ⚽

17 . . . . b) & c) ⚽ ⚽

18 . . . . c) ⚽

19 . . . . c) ⚽

20 . . . . a) ⚽

21 . . . . b)

22 . . . . a) b) d) e)

23 . . . . b)

24 . . . . b) Under 7s & 8s

                c) Under 9s & 10s

25 . . . . a)

26 . . . . a)

27 . . . . a) Under 7s & 8s

              b) Under 9s & 10s

28 . . . . a)

29 . . . . a)

30 . . . . a)

31 . . . . a)

32 . . . . b)

33 . . . . a) & c)

34 . . . . b)

35 . . . . a)

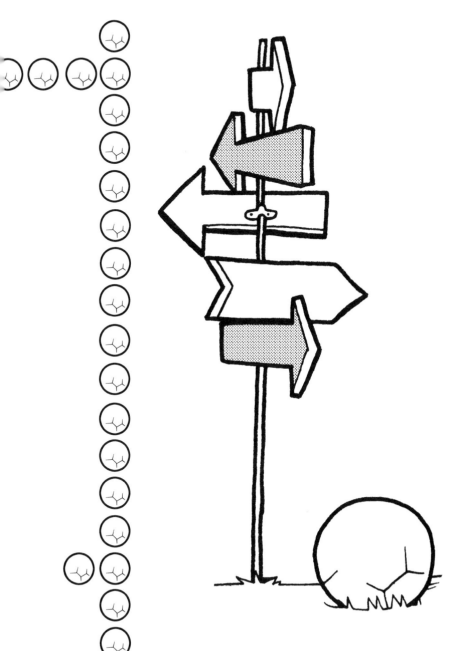

36 . . . . c)

37 . . . . a)

38 . . . . a)

39 . . . . a)

40 . . . . b)

41 . . . . b)

42 . . . . c)

43 . . . . b)

44 . . . . a)

45 . . . . b)

46 . . . . b) & d)

47 . . . . a)

48 . . . . c)

49 . . . . a)

50 . . . . b)

51 . . . . b)

52 . . . . . . a) b) d) e)

53 . . . . c)

54 . . . . b)

55 . . . . b)

56 . . . . c)

57 . . . . b) & c)

58 . . . . c) & d)

To give you an idea of how well you now know the Laws:-

> **If you scored**
>
> **up to 40**
> try again. Practice makes perfect !
>
> **40 – 50**
> you probably know more than your dad
>
> **50 – 60**
> you probably know more than your manager
>
> **over 60**
> you could probably qualify as a referee when you get older

If you need more Mini Soccer info, visit **www.tjfc.org.uk**, or check into the Football Association's site at **www.the-fa.org**.

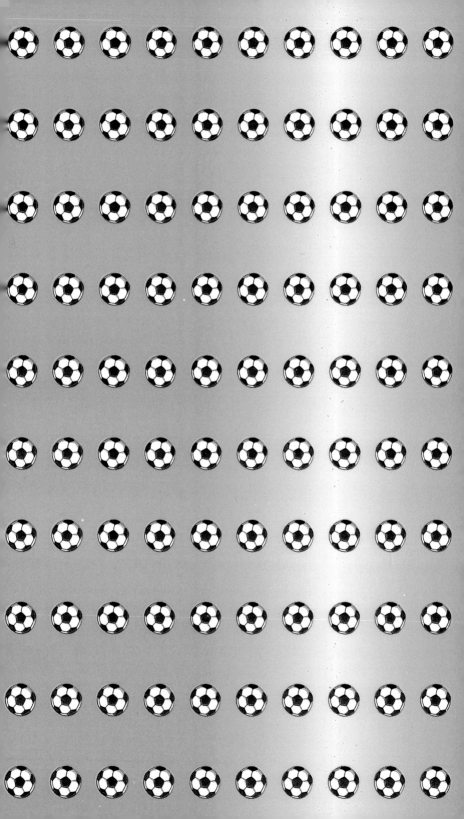